motets

mixed voices **a cappella**

John Kelleher

BOOSEY&HAWKES

Boosey & Hawkes Music Publishers Ltd
www.boosey.com

Published by Boosey & Hawkes Music Publishers Ltd
Aldwych House
71–91 Aldwych
London
WC2B 4HN

www.boosey.com

AN IMAGEM COMPANY

ISMN 979-0-060-12937-7
ISBN 978-1-78454-028-9

First printed 2014

Printed in England by The Halstan Printing Group, Amersham, Bucks

Cover design: Deutsche Grammophon GmbH, Berlin, adapted by RF Deisgn UK Limited
Cover picture: Andrea Vizzini, *Il Luogo degli Angeli*. © Andrea Vizzini

Karl Jenkins photo: Rhys Frampton

Music origination by Jon Bunker and The Note Factory

CONTENTS

MOTETS

PREFACE

This album of *Motets* marks the year of my 70th birthday and fifty years of my career in music.

A motet is a piece of sacred music for unaccompanied voices. The album includes movements taken from my extended works reconceived for this format together with some pieces that are newly composed.

From *The Armed Man: a Mass for Peace* I chose *Benedictus*, *Agnus Dei* and the closing chorale, *God shall wipe away all tears*.

Healing Light, *Peace, peace!* and *Dona nobis pacem* are from *The Peacemakers*.

Pie Jesu and *In paradisum* are from *Requiem*.

Ave verum corpus, originally written for Bryn Terfel, is from *Stabat Mater*. From the same work comes *And the Mother did weep*, itself an adaptation of *Amaté adea* from *Adiemus: Songs of Sanctuary*.

I have also revisited *Adiemus: Songs of Sanctuary* with *Cantate Domino* and *Ave Maria*, reworkings of *Adiemus* and *Hymn* respectively.

I'll make music and *Laudamus te* are from *Gloria*, while *Lullay* comes from *Stella natalis*.

Exsultate, jubilate is based on *Palladio*, a 'retro' instrumental piece inspired by the Italian architect of the same name.

Of the new pieces *The Shepherd* and *Nunc dimittis* are taken from *The Healer: a Cantata for St Luke*, which was commissioned by Grayshott Concerts for première in 2014. *Locus iste* was composed merely a week before the album was recorded by Polyphony and Stephen Layton.

Motets is dedicated to my son Jody.

Karl Jenkins
March 2014

Late one night in 1997, across a dark and deserted St Mark's Square, Venice, I saw a painting, lit like a beacon, drawing me inexorably to the window of Galleria Ravagnan. It made a deep impression on me, and my musician wife, Carol, remarked that it looked like my music sounded. I returned the next day, bought the painting and began a firm friendship with gallery owner Luciano Ravagnan. On a return visit, a year or so later, I met and befriended the artist, Andrea Vizzini, only for us both to discover that he, not knowing who had bought his painting, had been painting to my music!

The album cover is a painting by this eminent Italian artist, titled Il Luogo degli Angeli ('the place of the angels') and, as Stephen Layton remarked, is "the perfect doorway to what lies inside".

KJ

I'll make music (from *Gloria*)

Lord and Master, I'll sing a song to you,
on the ten-string lyre I'll make music.

Lord and Master, let your thoughts fall like rain
and just like showers on new grass.

We'll play for you with harps and trumpets,
we'll sing some psalms in praise of you.

Lord and Master, let your words descend like dew
and just like droplets on tender leaves.

We'll play for you with harps and trumpets,
we'll sing some psalms in praise of you.

I'll make music, I shall make new music,
I shall make music for you.

Deuteronomy 32:2, Psalm 144:9 and
1 Chronicles 13:8, adapted by Karl Jenkins

Cantate Domino (arrangement of 'Adiemus'
from *Adiemus: Songs of Sanctuary*)

Alleluia. Cantate Domino canticum novum.
Alleluia. Jubilate Deo omnis terra: servite
  Domino in lætitia.
Alleluia. Cantate et exsultate et psallite
  Regem regum et hymnum dicite Deo.
Alleluia.

Alleluia. Sing to the Lord a new song.
Alleluia. Be joyful in the Lord, all the earth: serve
  the Lord in gladness.
Alleluia. Sing and exult, and sing psalms to the King
  of Kings.
Alleluia.

Text from Psalms 46, 95, 99 (Vulgate)
English translation by Edward Tambling

Laudamus te (from *Gloria*)

Laudamus te. Benedicimus te. Adoramus te.
Glorificamus te. Gratias agimus tibi propter
magnam gloriam tuam.

We praise you. We bless you. We adore you. We
glorify you. We give thanks to you for your great glory.

Text from the Latin Mass

Benedictus (from *The Armed Man: a Mass
for Peace*)

Benedictus qui venit in nomine Domini.
Hosanna in excelsis.

Blessed is he who comes in the name of the Lord.
Hosanna in the highest.

Text from the Latin Mass

The Shepherd (from *The Healer*)

How sweet is the Shepherd's sweet lot!
From the morn to the evening he strays;
He shall follow his sheep all the day,
And his tongue shall be fillèd with praise.

For he hears the lamb's innocent call,
And he hears the ewe's tender reply.
He is watchful while they are in peace,
For they know when their Shepherd is nigh.

William Blake 1757–1827, Songs of Innocence

Ave Maria (arrangement of 'Hymn' from
Adiemus: Songs of Sanctuary)

Ave maria, gratia plena, Dominus tecum.
Benedicta tu in mulieribus, et benedictus
fructus ventris tui Jesus.

Sancta Maria, Mater Dei, ora pro nobis
peccatoribus nunc et in hora mortis nostræ.

Amen.

Hail Mary, full of grace, the Lord is with you.
You are blessed among women, and blessed is
Jesus, the fruit of your womb.

Holy Mary, Mother of God, pray for us sinners now
and at the hour of our death.

Amen.

Latin prayer (from the Gospel
according to St Luke)
English translation by Edward Tambling

Ave verum corpus (from *Stabat Mater*)

Ave verum corpus natum
de Maria Virgine.
Vere passum, immolatum
in cruce pro homine.
Cujus latus perforatum
fluxit aqua et sanguine.
Esto nobis prægustatum
mortis in examine.

Jesu dulcis! Jesu pie,
Fili Mariæ.
Amen.

Hail, true body,
born of the Virgin Mary,
truly suffered and slain
on a cross for man.
Whose pierced side
poured forth water and blood.
Be to us a foretaste
in the agony of death.

Sweet Jesus! Kind Jesus,
Son of Mary.
Amen.

Latin prayer attributed to
Pope Innocent VI (c1295–1362)
English translation by Edward Tambling

Agnus Dei (from *The Armed Man: a Mass for Peace*)

Agnus Dei qui tollis peccata mundi
miserere nobis.
Agnus Dei,
dona nobis pacem.

Lamb of God, who takes away the sins of the world,
have mercy on us.
Lamb of God,
grant us peace.

Text from the Latin Mass

Healing Light (from *The Peacemakers*)

Deep peace of the running wave to you,
Deep peace of the flowing air to you,
Deep peace of the quiet earth to you.
Amen.

Deep peace of the shining stars to you,
Deep peace of the gentle night to you,
Moon and stars pour their healing light on you.
Amen.

Anon

Locus iste

Locus iste a Deo factus est,
inæstimabile sacramentum,
irreprehensibilis est.

Deus, cui adestat angelorum chorus,
exaudi preces servorum tuorum.

This place was made by God,
an invaluable sacrament,
it is blameless.

O God, for whom the chorus of angels is present,
hear the prayers of your servants.

Gradual of the Mass for the
Dedication of a Church
English translation by Edward Tambling

Pie Jesu (from *Requiem*)

Pie Jesu Domine, dona eis requiem
    sempiternam.

Sweet Lord Jesus, grant them everlasting rest.

Text from the Requiem Mass

Exsultate, jubilate (arrangement of *Palladio*, first movement)

Exsultate, jubilate,
O vos animæ beatæ,
exsultate, jubilate,
dulcia cantica canendo;
cantui vestro respondendo
psallant æthera cum me.

Exult, be joyful,
O you happy souls,
exult, be joyful,
in the singing of sweet songs;
and in response to your song
may the heavens sing psalms with me.

Anon
English translation by Edward Tambling

God shall wipe away all tears (from *The Armed Man: a Mass for Peace*)

God shall wipe away all tears
and there shall be no more death,
neither sorrow nor crying,
neither shall there be any more pain.
Praise the Lord.

Text from Revelation 21:4

And the Mother did weep (from *Stabat Mater* and *Adiemus: Songs of Sanctuary*)

And the Mother did weep.
She did weep, and she did weep.
Vehaeym bachetah (*Hebrew*)
Lacrimavit Mater (*Latin*)
Warkath hahi imma (*Aramaic*)
Kai eklausen he meter (*Greek*)

Karl Jenkins

Lullay (from *Stella natalis*)

Lullay, my loved one, so peaceful, so small,
sleep while the world awakes.
Under the bright star just over your stall,
safe as the morning breaks.

Lullay, lullay *etc*

Jesu, so peaceful, asleep in the hay,
rest till you hear us call.
One day you'll carry our sorrows away,
soon you will save us all.

Jesu, Jesu *etc*

Lullay, my loved one, so peaceful, so small,
rest till the storms pass by.

Lullay, lullay *etc*

Carol Barratt

Peace, peace! (from *The Peacemakers*)

Peace, peace! he is not dead, he doth not sleep –
He hath awakened from the dream of life –
'Tis we, who lost in stormy visions, keep
With phantoms an unprofitable strife.

Shalom. Shanti. Salam. Shlama.

*Percy Bysshe Shelley (1792–1822),
from* Elegy on the Death of John Keats;
'peace' in Hebrew, Sanskrit, Arabic and Aramaic

In Paradisum (from *Requiem*)

In paradisum deducant te angeli,
in tuo adventu suscipiant te martyres,
et perducant te in civitatem sanctam
    Jerusalem.
Chorus angelorum te suscipiant,
et cum Lazaro quondam paupere
æternam habeas requiem.

*May angels lead you into paradise,
and may martyrs receive you at your arrival,
and may they lead you into the holy city Jerusalem.
May a chorus of angels receive you,
and with Lazarus who was once a pauper
may you have eternal rest.*

*Text from the Requiem Mass
English translation by Edward Tambling*

Dona nobis pacem (from *The Peacemakers*)

Lord give us peace, O Lord, give us peace.
Dona nobis pacem.

The world is but one country, and mankind
its citizens. We are all fruits of one tree and
leaves of one branch.

*Text from the Ordinary of the
Mass (English & Latin);
Bahá'u'lláh (1817–92)*

Nunc dimittis (from *The Healer*)

Nunc dimittis servum tuum, Domine,
secundum verbum tuum in pace:

quia viderunt oculi mei salutare tuum quod
parasti ante faciem omnium populorum:

lumen ad revelationem gentium,
et gloriam plebis tuæ Israel.

*Now you let your servant depart in peace, O Lord,
according to your word.*

*For my eyes have seen your salvation which you
have prepared before the face of all peoples:*

*a light to lighten the nations,
and the glory of your people Israel.*

*Luke 2:29–32
English translation by Edward Tambling*

PERFORMANCE NOTE

All pieces are intended to be performed *a cappella*.
Where an accompaniment for piano or organ is
provided it is entirely optional.

Recorded on DG CD 00289 479 3232 by Stephen Layton and Polyphony

Polyphony

Soprano
Rachel Ambrose Evans
   (solo on *Dona nobis pacem*)
Zoe Brown
Alison Hill
Eloise Irving
Hannah Partridge
Louise Prickett
Katie Thomas
Genevieve Wakelin
Amy Wood

Alto
Hannah Cooke
Ruth Kiang
Amy Lyddon-Towl
Fiona Mckay
Eleanor Minney
Katherine Nicholson
Katie Schofield

Tenor
Guy Cutting
Jonathan English
Christopher Hann
Benedict Hymas
David Lee
Gautam Rangarajan

Bass
Richard Bannan
Michael Craddock
William Dawes
William Gaunt
Gavin Horsley
Dominic Kraemer
Nicholas Mogg
Richard Savage
Laurence Williams

I'LL MAKE MUSIC

a cappella motet for SSAATTB

Deuteronomy 32:2, Psalm 144:9
& 1 Chronicles 13:8
adapted by Karl Jenkins

KARL JENKINS

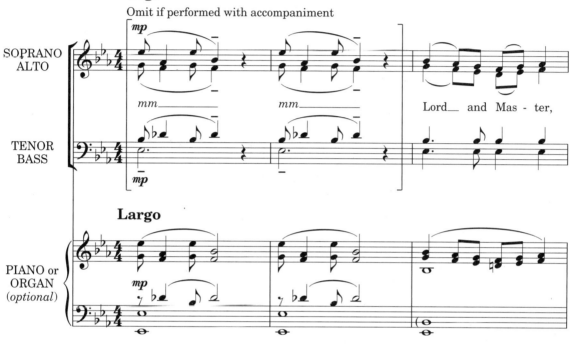

2

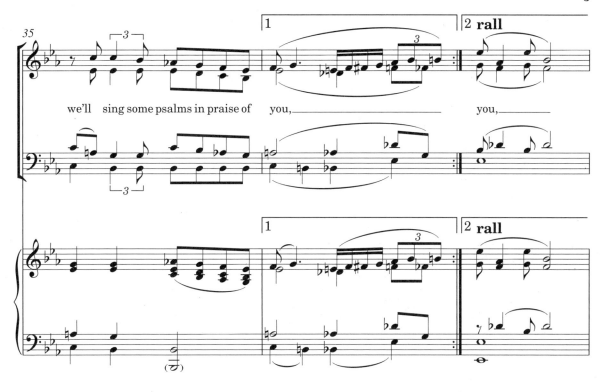

we'll sing some psalms in praise of you,_____ you,_____

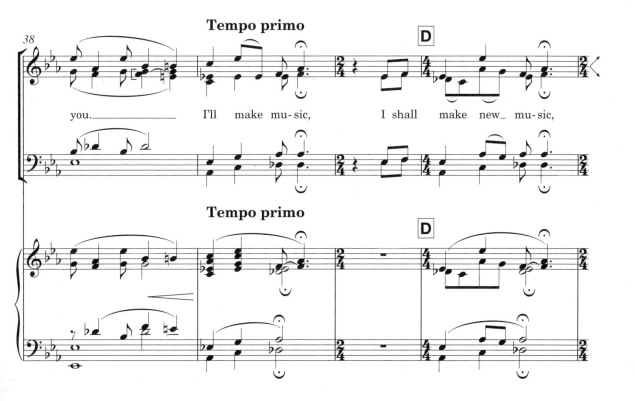

you._____ I'll make mu-sic, I shall make new_ mu-sic,

CANTATE DOMINO

a cappella motet for SSATB

Words from
Ps 46, 95, 99
(Vulgate)

KARL JENKINS

LAUDAMUS TE

a cappella motet for SSATB(B)

Words from
the Latin Mass

KARL JENKINS

Organ omit lower octave

16

BENEDICTUS

a cappella motet for SATBB

Words from
the Latin Mass

KARL JENKINS

Molto largo

1st time only

20

THE SHEPHERD

a cappella motet for SATTB

WILLIAM BLAKE
(1757–1827)

KARL JENKINS

★Small notes for Organ Pedals only

24

28

AVE MARIA

a cappella motet for SSAATB

Latin prayer,
from St Luke's Gospel

KARL JENKINS

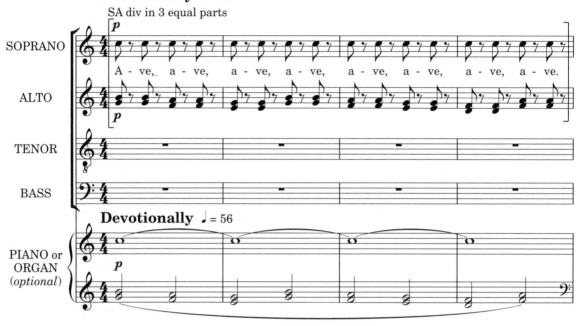

34

AVE VERUM CORPUS

a cappella motet for SATB

Latin prayer
attrib Pope Innocent VI
(*c*1295–1362)

KARL JENKINS

★Here and in similar instances organ may tie repeated notes.

38

42

AGNUS DEI

a cappella motet for SSATTBB(B)

Words from
the Latin Mass

KARL JENKINS

Organ: no 16'

★Optional doubling in addition to full size notes

44

HEALING LIGHT

a cappella motet for SSAATB

ANON

KARL JENKINS

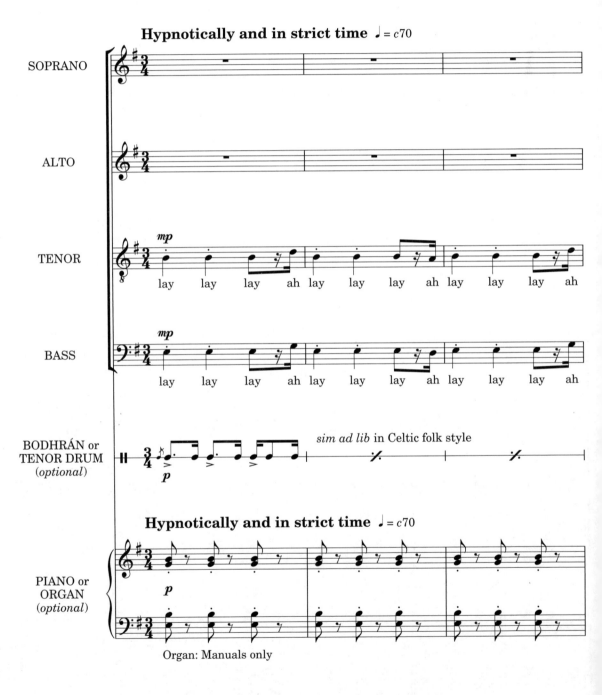

57

58

LOCUS ISTE

a cappella motet for SAATTB(BB)

Gradual of the Mass
for the Dedication
of a Church

KARL JENKINS

PIE JESU

a cappella motet for SATB

KARL JENKINS

Words from the
Requiem Mass

This page is left blank intentionally

EXSULTATE, JUBILATE

a cappella motet for SSAATBB

ANON

KARL JENKINS

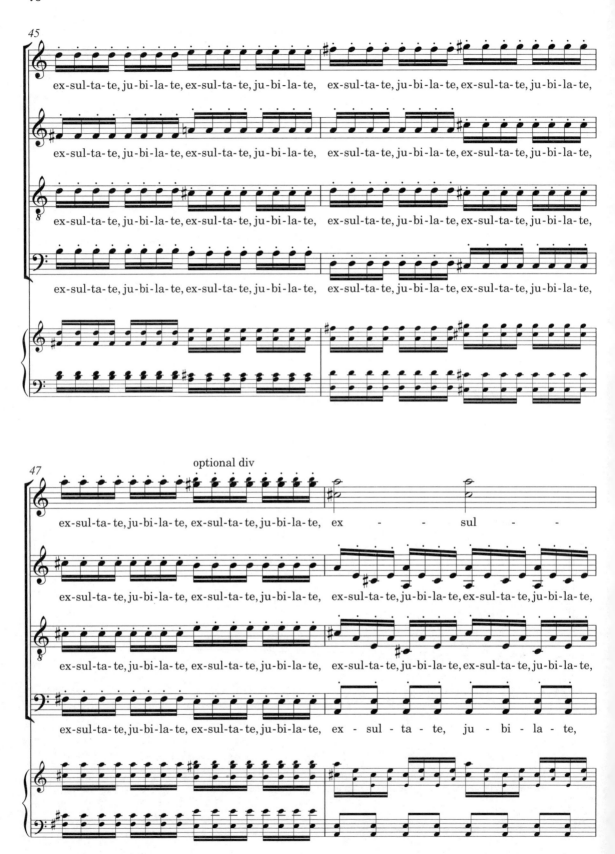

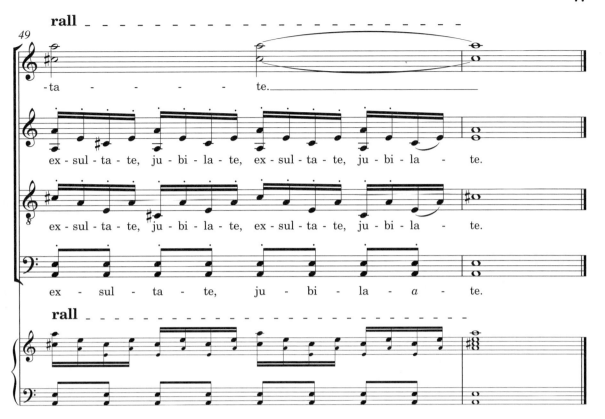

GOD SHALL WIPE AWAY ALL TEARS

a cappella motet for SSAATBB

KARL JENKINS

Words from
Revelation 21:4

★ Optional

AND THE MOTHER DID WEEP

a cappella motet for SATB(B)

Words & music by
KARL JENKINS

If performed with accompaniment, bar 1 of the keyboard part, left hand only,
may be used as an introduction.

82

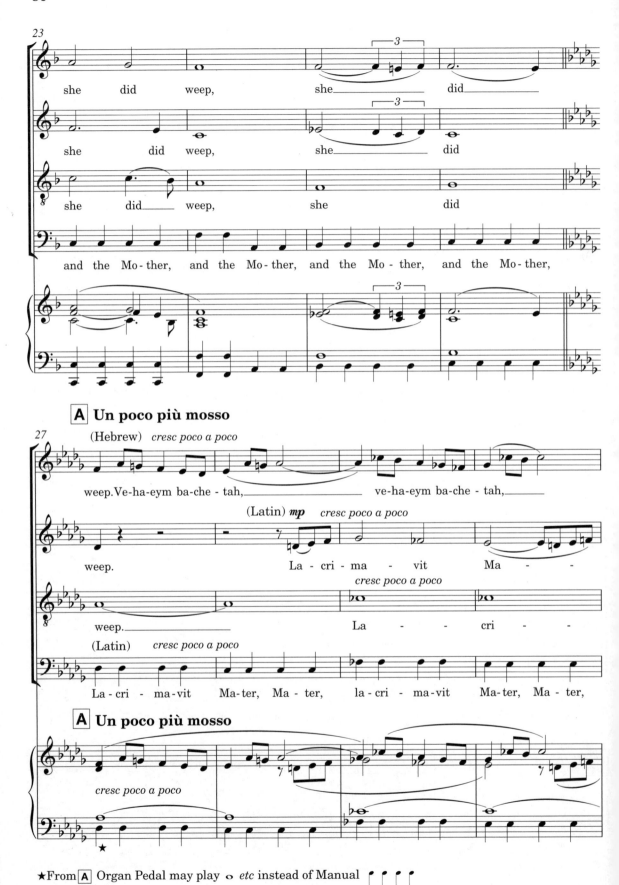

★From Ⓐ Organ Pedal may play o *etc* instead of Manual ♩♩♩♩

88

Organ as at the beginning

LULLAY

a cappella motet for SATB

CAROL BARRATT

KARL JENKINS

94

Omit if sung with accompaniment

PEACE, PEACE!

PERCY BYSSHE SHELLEY
(1792–1822)

a cappella motet for SSAATTB

KARL JENKINS

Piano may add LH lower octave.
Organ may double RH chords an octave lower in LH.

102

IN PARADISUM

Words from the
Requiem Mass

a cappella motet for S(S)AATB

KARL JENKINS

110

DONA NOBIS PACEM

a cappella motet for S solo & SSAATB

The Ordinary of the Mass;
BAHÁ'U'LLÁ (1817–92)

KARL JENKINS

Organ: tie repeated notes and omit lower octaves as appropriate.

NUNC DIMITTIS

a cappella motet for SSAATB

LUKE 2:29–32

KARL JENKINS

★Optional solo part. If sung by choir SA div in 3.

120

Organ omit lower octave

★Optional solo part. If sung by choir SA div in 3.